The HABITS of HAPPINESS

DAILYHOPE
WITH RICK WARREN

Habits of Happiness

Published by Daily Hope
23182 Arroyo Vista
Rancho Santa Margarita, CA 92688
www.pastorrick.com

ISBN: 978-1-4228-0338-7

Printed and bound in the United States of America.

CONTENTS

UNDERSTANDING YOUR STUDY GUIDE

Here is a brief explanation of the features of this study guide.

CHECKING IN: You will open each meeting with an opportunity for everyone to check in with each other about how you are doing with the weekly assignments. Accountability is a key to success in this study!

KEY VERSE: Each week you will find a key verse or Scripture passage for your group to read together. If someone in the group has a different translation, ask them to read it aloud so the group can get a bigger picture of the meaning of the passage.

VIDEO LESSON: There is a video lesson for the group to watch together each week. Fill in the blanks in the lesson outlines as you watch the video, and be sure to refer back to these outlines during your discussion time.

DISCOVERY QUESTIONS: Each video segment is complemented by several questions for group discussion. Please don't feel pressured to discuss every single question. There is no reason to rush through the answers. Give everyone ample opportunity to share their thoughts. If you don't get through all of the discussion questions, that's okay.

PUTTING IT INTO PRACTICE: This is where the rubber meets the road. We don't want to be just hearers of the Word. We also need to be doers of the Word (James 1:22). These assignments are application exercises that will help you put into practice the truths you have discussed in the lesson.

PRAYER DIRECTION: At the end of each session you will find suggestions for your group prayer time. Praying together is one of the greatest privileges of small group life. Please don't take it for granted.

A Tip for the Host

The study guide material is meant to be your servant, not your master. The point is not to race through the sessions; the point is to take time to let God work in your lives. Nor is it necessary to "go around the circle" before you move on to the next question. Give people the freedom to speak, but don't insist on it. Your group will enjoy deeper, more open sharing and discussion if people don't feel pressured to speak up.

HOW TO USE THIS VIDEO CURRICULUM

Follow these simple steps for a successful small group meeting:

- Open your group meeting by using the **Checking In** section of your study guide.

- Watch the video lesson together and follow along in the outlines in this study guide. Each video lesson is about 25 minutes long.

- Complete the rest of the discussion materials for each session. Be sure to review the **Putting It Into Practice** section and commit to fulfilling any action steps before your next session.

- Close your time together by following the **Prayer Direction** suggestions.

GROWING HEALTHY RELATIONSHIPS

CHECKING IN

If this is your first time to meet as a group, or if you have any new group members, be sure to introduce yourselves.

Think of someone who has been an encouragement to you, who expected the best of you. How did that person's confident expectations influence your life?

KEY VERSE

"Every time I think of you, I give thanks to my God."

Philippians 1:3 (NLT)

FIVE LAWS OF HAPPINESS

1. Don't look for happiness;

_____.

2. Happiness is not _____.

3. _____ create my happiness.

4. Happiness based on happenings is _____. But happiness built on habits is _____.

5. _____ habits are as addicting as bad habits.

"This letter is from Paul and Timothy, slaves of Christ Jesus. I am writing to all of God's holy people in Philippi who belong to Christ Jesus, including the elders and deacons. May God our Father and the Lord Jesus Christ give you grace and peace.

Every time I think of you, I give thanks to my God. Whenever I pray, I make my requests for all of you with joy, for you have been my partners in spreading the Good News about Christ from the time you first heard it until now. And I am certain that God, who began the good work within you, will continue his work until it is finally finished on the day when Christ Jesus returns.

So it is right that I should feel as I do about all of you, for you have a special place in my heart. You share with me the special favor of God, both in my imprisonment and in defending and confirming the truth of the Good News. God knows how much I love you and long for you with the tender compassion of Christ Jesus.

I pray that your love will overflow more and more, and that you will keep on growing in knowledge and understanding. For I want you to understand what really matters, so that you may live pure and blameless lives until the day of Christ's return. May you always be filled with the fruit of your salvation — the righteous character produced in your life by Jesus Christ — for this will bring much glory and praise to God."

Philippians 1:1-11 (NLT)

FOUR RELATIONAL HABITS OF HAPPINESS

1. I must _____ for the people in my life.

> *"Every time I think of you, I give thanks to my God."*
>
> **Philippians 1:3 (NLT)**
>
> *"I thank God for the help you gave me . . ."*
>
> **Philippians 1:5 (NCV)**

Happiness Hint: Remember _____, and _____.

2. _____ for the people in my life.

> *"Whenever I pray, I make my requests for all of you with joy."*
>
> **Philippians 1:4 (NLT)**

Happiness Hint: The quickest way to change a bad relationship to a good one, _____ _____.

> "And this is my prayer: that your love may abound more and more in knowledge and depth of insight, so that you may be able to discern what is best and may be pure and blameless for the day of Christ, filled with the fruit of righteousness that comes through Jesus Christ—to the glory and praise of God."
>
> **Philippians 1:9-11 (NIV)**

Four Things to Pray for People

- They will _____.
- They will _____.
- They will _____.
- They will _____.

> ". . . filled with the fruit of righteousness that comes through Jesus Christ—to the glory and praise of God."
>
> **Philippians 1:11 (NIV)**

> "The fruit of the Spirit is love, joy, peace, patience, kindness, goodness, faithfulness, gentleness and self-control."
>
> **Galatians 5:22-23a (NIV)**

3. _____ **from people**

in my life.

> "... being confident of this, that he who began a good work in you will carry it on to completion until the day of Christ Jesus."
>
> **Philippians 1:6 (NIV)**

Three Ways Paul Brought the Best out of People

- He _____.

- He _____.

- He was _____.

Happiness Hint: Celebrate _____

_____ **rather than judging them for**

_____.

> "It is right for me to feel this way about all of you, since I have you in my heart."
>
> **Philippians 1:7a (NIV)**

4. Love people in my life

_____.

> *"God is my witness that I tell the truth when I say that my deep love for you all comes from the heart of Christ Jesus himself."*
>
> **Philippians 1:8 (TEV)**

DISCOVERY QUESTIONS

1. Pastor Rick teaches that happiness is not the goal but rather the result of developing Christ-like relational habits. Which habits are already part of your daily routine? Which one is the most difficult for you to practice?

2. One of the Happiness Hints teaches to celebrate how far people have come rather than judging them for how far they still have to go. Why is this easier said than done?

3. Often when people are irritating, you want them to change. Instead of wishing they would change, you are called to pray for them. Have you ever tried doing this? If so, how did it help?

4. People need others to believe in them, because it's how everyone changes. Acceptance always precedes transformation. How will you apply this truth to one of your most important relationships this week?

PUTTING IT INTO PRACTICE

Human beings are not grateful by nature. The longer you know someone, the more likely you are to take that person for granted. God's antidote for this is gratitude. Discuss ideas that will help you begin to develop a habit of expressing gratitude for the people in your life. If you already do this, share your experience with the group.

PRAYER DIRECTION

Discuss how your group wants to approach prayer during this six-week study. Encourage everyone to share ideas. Consider asking if anyone has a desire to be a prayer champion for the group. This could include summarizing and sending out prayer requests weekly, but you can openly talk about other ways to support each other in prayer.

HOW TO BE HAPPY NO MATTER WHAT

CHECKING IN

Last week in session 1, Pastor Rick taught you the Four Habits of Happiness. Discuss the progress everyone made. Which habit was the easiest to practice? Which was the hardest?

KEY VERSE

"Whatever happens, conduct yourselves in a manner worthy of the gospel of Christ."

Philippians 1:27a (NIV)

FOUR COMMON BARRIERS TO HAPPINESS

1. _____

2. _____

3. _____

4. _____

"I want you to know, my dear brothers and sisters, that everything that has happened to me here has helped to spread the Good News. For everyone here, including the whole palace guard, knows that I am in chains because of Christ. And because of my imprisonment, most of the believers here have gained confidence and boldly speak God's message without fear.

It's true that some are preaching out of jealousy and rivalry. But others preach about Christ with pure motives. They preach because they love me, for they know I have been appointed to defend the Good News. Those others do not have pure motives as they preach about Christ. They preach with selfish ambition, not sincerely, intending to make my chains more painful to me. But that doesn't matter. Whether their motives are false or genuine, the message about Christ is being preached either way, so I rejoice. And I will continue to rejoice. For I know that as you pray for me and the Spirit of Jesus Christ helps me, this will lead to my deliverance.

For I fully expect and hope that I will never be ashamed, but that I will continue to be bold for Christ, as I have been in the past. And I trust that my life will bring honor to Christ, whether I live or die. For to me, living means living for Christ, and dying is even better. But if I live, I can do more fruitful work for Christ. So I really don't know which is better. I'm torn between two desires: I long to go and be with Christ, which would be far better for me. But for your sakes, it is better that I continue to live.

Knowing this, I am convinced that I will remain alive so I can continue to help all of you grow and experience the joy of your faith. And when I come to you again, you will have even more reason to take pride in Christ Jesus because of what he is doing through me.

Above all, you must live as citizens of heaven, conducting yourselves in a manner worthy of the Good News about Christ. Then, whether I come and see you again or only hear about you, I will know that you are standing together with one spirit and one purpose, fighting together for the faith, which is the Good News. Don't be intimidated in any way by your enemies. This will be a sign to them that they are going to be destroyed, but that you are going to be saved, even by God himself. For you have been given not only the privilege of trusting in Christ but also the privilege of suffering for him. We are in this struggle together. You have seen my struggle in the past, and you know that I am still in the midst of it."

Philippians 1:12-30 (NLT)

YOU CAN BE HAPPY IF YOU...

1. Look at every problem from

_____.

> *"I want you to know, my dear brothers and sisters, that everything that has happened to me here has helped to spread the Good News."*
>
> **Philippians 1:12 (NLT)**

Anytime you face problems in faith:

- It's a _____.

> *"For everyone here, including the whole palace guard, knows that I am in chains because of Christ."*
>
> **Philippians 1:13 (NLT)**

- It's an _____.

> *"Because of my imprisonment, most of the believers here have gained confidence and boldly speak God's message without fear."*
>
> **Philippians 1:14 (NLT)**

2. Never let others _____

_____.

Four Kinds of People

- Critics

> *"Of course some of them preach Christ because they are jealous and quarrelsome."*
>
> **Philippians 1:15a (TEV)**

Happiness Hint: _____

_____.

- Comrades

> *"Others [preach Christ] from genuine good will. They do so from love, because they know that God has given me the work of defending the gospel."*
>
> **Philippians 1:15b-16 (TEV)**

- Competitors

> *"Others do not proclaim Christ sincerely, but from a spirit of selfish ambition."*
>
> **Philippians 1:17a (TEV)**

- Conspirators

3. _____ to work things out.

Four Sources of Strength

1. I have God's _____ on my problems.

2. I have people _____ for me.

3. I have the _____ helping me.

4. I have faith that _____ .

4. If I stay _____, not my problem.

24

"For to me, to live is Christ and to die is gain."

Philippians 1:21 (NIV)

How *you* fill in the blank will determine your happiness:

"For *me* to live is _____."

DISCOVERY QUESTIONS

1. There are four common barriers to joy. These joy killers are: pain, picky people, pressure (internal or external), and problems. Which barriers have been your most common stumbling blocks?

2. Paul chose to rejoice no matter what. Have you been rejoicing lately? If so, share your experience. If not, what's stopping you?

3. Share an experience when you learned that your faith was a witness to an unbeliever. What effect did this have on you?

4. In Philippians 1:15-17, Paul describes four kinds of people: critics, comrades, competitors, and conspirators. In which of these roles have you found yourself? Did you realize it at the time?

5. After learning how Paul approached his life with fearless faith, what one thing can you change now that will boost your happiness?

PUTTING IT INTO PRACTICE

How did you fill in the blank: "For me to live is: _____"? In other words, what sometimes replaces God for the number 1 place in your life? As a group, list some practical steps for keeping God first. Because happiness is a habit, have each group member pick one suggestion to practice during the week.

PRAYER DIRECTION

Take turns sharing in one sentence how Paul's purpose and perspective have influenced yours. As a group, close in prayer, committing to practice the four habits this week and asking for God's help to approach every problem from his perspective and with eyes of faith. Ask God to use the people in your group to witness to unbelievers and encourage believers in the coming week.

THE HUMBLE PATH TO HAPPINESS

CHECKING IN

Unresolved conflict hurts relationships. Are you in the midst of a conflict right now? How is it impacting your happiness?

KEY VERSE

"When you do things, do not let selfishness or pride be your guide. Instead, be humble and give more honor to others than to yourselves."

Philippians 2:3 (NCV)

The habit of humility is the key to reducing conflict in your life, because pride is the thing that causes conflict.

"Pride only leads to arguments."

Proverbs 13:10a (NCV)

"Does your life in Christ give you strength? Does his love comfort you? Do we share together in the spirit? Do you have mercy and kindness? If so, make me very happy by having the same thoughts, sharing the same love, and having one mind and purpose. When you do things, do not let selfishness or pride be your guide. Instead, be humble and give more honor to others than to yourselves. Don't be interested only in your own life, but be interested in the lives of others.

In your lives you must think and act like Christ Jesus. Christ himself was like God in everything. But he did not think that being equal with God was something to be demanded. Instead, he gave up his place with God and made himself nothing. He was born to be a human being and became a servant. While he was living on earth as a man, he humbled himself and became fully obedient to God the Father, even when that caused his death — death on a cross. So then God raised him to the highest place. God made his name greater than every other name so that every knee will bow to the name of Jesus — everyone in heaven, on earth, and under the earth. One day everyone will confess that Jesus Christ is Lord and bring glory to the Father."

Philippians 2:1-11 (NCV)

FOUR KINDS OF HARMONY

1. _____

2. _____

3. _____

4. _____

FOUR HABITS FOR REDUCING CONFLICT

1. Never let _____ be my guide.

"Do nothing out of selfish ambition or vain conceit."

Philippians 2:3a (NIV)

"Where there is jealousy and selfishness, there will be confusion and every kind of evil."

James 3:16 (ERV)

2. Be _____, or I'll stumble!

> *"Instead, be humble and give more honor to others than to yourself."*
>
> **Philippians 2:3b (NCV)**

3. Learn the lost art of

_____!

> *"Do not be interested only in your own life, but be interested in the lives of others."*
>
> **Philippians 2:4 (NCV)**

4. Ask, "What would _____ do?"

> *"Your attitude should be the same as that of Christ Jesus."*
>
> **Philippians 2:5 (NIV)**

THREE EXAMPLES OF ACTING LIKE JESUS

1. _____ what I think I deserve.

> *"Though he was God, [he] did not demand and cling to his rights as God, but laid aside his mighty power and glory..."*
>
> **Philippians 2:6-7a (TLB)**

2. Look for ways that I can _____.

> *"[He] took the nature of a servant. He became like a human being."*
>
> **Philippians 2:7b (GNT)**

3. _____ even when it's painful.

> *"And when he was living as a man, he humbled himself and was ully obedient to God, even when that caused his death—death on a cross."*
>
> **Philippians 2:8 (NCV)**

> *"Therefore God exalted him to the highest place and gave him the name that is above every name, that at the name of Jesus every knee should bow, in heaven and on earth and under the earth, and every tongue acknowledge that Jesus Christ is Lord, to the glory of God the Father."*
>
> **Philippians 2:9-11 (NIV)**

DISCOVERY QUESTIONS

1. Jesus modeled harmony and humility. How do you model these qualities in your life? What makes developing and maintaining these habits so difficult?

2. When is the last time your "I" problem caused a conflict with someone? How long did it take before you realized your pride had lured you down the wrong path? Share how you resolved the conflict.

3. Philippians 2:3 says, "When you do things, do not let selfishness or pride be your guide. Instead, be humble and give more honor to others than to yourselves" (NCV). What does it mean to give more honor to others than yourself? If you went through a full day with this as the "theme" of your day, would you do anything differently?

4. Humility is not thinking less of yourself. Humility is thinking of yourself less. Notice the difference? The more you think about other people, the more humble you become. Although this can be easier said than done, talk with your group about practical ways to practice this perspective in the coming week.

5. Pastor Rick teaches that in God's economy, the way up is down. In other words, the more you give your life away in service, the more God blesses you with honor. Share an experience when you blessed someone with your service. What did you learn in the process?

PUTTING IT INTO PRACTICE

The convenience of mobile technology continues to affect our relational health. We pay attention to our devices more than we pay attention to people. We're missing opportunities to connect and reach out to others. Discuss different ways to reverse this trend, and intentionally make shifts toward reducing screen time and increasing people time this week.

PRAYER DIRECTION

Enter into your group prayer time thanking God in advance for his Word that reveals how to live in harmony and humility and avoid conflict in relationships. Pray for wisdom and guidance to begin practicing humility while learning how to pay more attention to others and develop the nature of a servant like Jesus.

HOW TO KEEP YOUR HEART HAPPY

CHECKING IN

Share how you did reducing your screen time last week. Were you able to increase your people time? What did you learn? How will you keep making progress in this area this week?

KEY VERSE

"Therefore, my dear friends, as you have always obeyed — not only in my presence, but now much more in my absence — continue to work out your salvation with fear and trembling, for it is God who works in you to will and to act in order to fulfill his good purpose."

Philippians 2:12-13 (NIV)

"Therefore, my dear friends, as you have always obeyed—not only in my presence, but now much more in my absence—continue to work out your salvation with fear and trembling, for it is God who works in you to will and to act in order to fulfill his good purpose. Do everything without grumbling or arguing, so that you may become blameless and pure, 'children of God without fault in a warped and crooked generation.' Then you will shine among them like stars in the sky as you hold firmly to the word of life. And then I will be able to boast on the day of Christ that I did not run or labor in vain. But even if I am being poured out like a drink offering on the sacrifice and service coming from your faith, I am glad and rejoice with all of you. So you too should be glad and rejoice with me."

Philippians 2:12-18 (NIV)

"For it is by grace you have been saved, through faith—and this is not from yourselves, it is the gift of God—not by works, so that no one can boast."

Ephesians 2:8-9 (NIV)

FIVE EXERCISES FOR A HAPPY HEART

1. Remember that God is _____ me, he's _____ me, and he's _____ me.

"For God is working in you, giving you the desire and the power to do what pleases him."

Philippians 2:13 (NLT)

*"I will not leave you as orphans; I will come to you . . . .
On that day you will realize that I am in my Father, and
you are in me, and I am in you."*

John 14:18, 20 (NIV)

"If God is for us, no one can defeat us."

Romans 8:31b (NCV)

2. _____ and

_____ .

*"In everything you do, stay away from complaining and arguing so
that no one can speak a word of blame against you."*

Philippians 2:14-15a (TLB)

3. Keep my _____ clear.

*". . . so that you may become blameless and pure, 'children of God
without fault in a warped and crooked generation. Then you will shine
among them like stars in the sky.'"*

Philippians 2:15 (NIV)

> *"Happy are those who live pure lives, who follow the Lord's teaching. Happy are those who keep his rules, who try to obey him with their whole heart."*
>
> **Psalm 119:1-2 (NCV)**

> *"Blessed are the pure in heart, for they shall see God."*
>
> **Matthew 5:8 (ESV)**

> *"What happiness for those whose guilt has been forgiven! What joys when sins are covered over! What relief for those who have confessed their sins and God has cleared their record."*
>
> **Psalm 32:1 (TLB)**

4. _____ God's Word and _____.

5. Use my life _____

by serving others.

> *"Inasmuch as ye have done it unto one of the least of these my brethren, ye have done it unto me."*
>
> **Matthew 25:40 (AKJV)**

"If you insist on saving your life, you will lose it. Only those who throw away their lives for my sake and for the sake of the Good News will ever know what it means to really live."

Mark 8:35 (TLB)

"And I will give you a new heart—I will give you new and right desires—and put a new spirit within you. I will take out your stony hearts of sin and give you new hearts of love."

Ezekiel 36:26 (TLB)

"Salvation is to be found through [Jesus] alone; in all the world there is no one else whom God has given who can save us."

Acts 4:12 (TEV)

DISCOVERY QUESTIONS

1. People often excuse themselves for all the mistakes they make, and they accuse others. What problem have you blamed on someone or something else, instead of making the choice to be happy?

2. Pastor Rick talked about the importance of *spiritual breathing* — the daily practice of breathing out your sins in confession and breathing in God's power and cleansing. This daily habit removes any of the "bad stuff" you may have acquired during the course of your day. How will you begin practicing this?

3. In serving others, you serve God. This act of love boosts happiness. How have you experienced this?

4. Everyone has spiritual coronary disease, but the good news is Dr. Jesus can give you a heart transplant when you need one. Who has a testimony about the healing he or she received from Dr. Jesus?

5. If you are already an expert in worrying, you can meditate. Meditation is simply thinking about God's Word over and over in your mind. Take the next few minutes and practice meditating and memorizing the key verse for this session:

"Therefore, my dear friends, as you have always obeyed — not only in my presence, but now much more in my absence — continue to work out your salvation with fear and trembling, for it is God who works in you to will and to act in order to fulfill his good purpose."

Philippians 2:12-13 (NIV)

PUTTING IT INTO PRACTICE

Developing the habits of happiness takes practice. To increase happiness and reduce fear, Pastor Rick encourages you to get up every morning and say, "God, I thank you that you're going to be *with me* today, you're going to be *in me* today, and you're going to be *for me* today." Write this down on a 4x6 card or piece of paper and take it home with you. Place it on your bedside table, and this week, start each day with this thankful prayer.

PRAYER DIRECTION

Individually, spend a few moments in silent prayer, asking God to help you develop and nurture these five exercises for a happy heart. As a group, praise God for his unfailing love and for providing the formula for creating a healthy, happy heart.

HOW TO KEEP FROM STRESSING OUT

CHECKING IN

How did your thankful prayer ("God is with me, in me, and for me") impact your happiness last week? Did you find yourself praying it more than once a day? Share your experience with the group.

KEY VERSE

"If you do this, you will experience God's peace, which is far more wonderful than the human mind can understand."

Philippians 4:7a (TLB)

WAYS TO KEEP FROM STRESSING OUT

1. _____ **about anything.**

> *"Never worry about anything."*
>
> **Philippians 4:6a (ISV)**

Four Reasons You Should Never Worry About Anything

1. Worry is _____.

> *"Therefore I tell you, do not worry about your life, what you will eat or drink; or about your body, what you will wear. Is not life more than food, and the body more than clothes?"*
>
> **Matthew 6:25 (NIV)**

2. Worry is _____.

> *"Look at the birds of the air; they do not sow or reap or store away in barns, and yet your heavenly Father feeds them. Are you not much more valuable than they?"*
>
> **Matthew 6:26 (NIV)**

3. Worry is _____.

4. Worry is _____.

> *"And if God cares so wonderfully for flowers that are here today and gone tomorrow, won't he more surely care for you, O men of little faith?"*
>
> **Matthew 6:30 (TLB)**

2. _____ about everything.

> *"Don't worry about anything, but in all your prayers ask God for what you need . . ."*
>
> **Philippians 4:6a (TEV)**

3. _____ in all things.

> *"Don't worry about anything, but in all your prayers ask God for what you need, always asking him with a thankful heart."*
>
> **Philippians 4:6 (TEV)**

4. Think about _____.

> *"Think about the things that are good and worthy of praise. Think about the things that are true and honorable and right and pure and beautiful and respected. If there is any excellence and if anything worthy of praise, dwell on these things."*
>
> **Philippians 4:8 (NCV/NASB)**

5. _____ with anything.

> *"I have learned how to be content with whatever I have. I know how to live on almost nothing or with everything. I have learned the secret of living in every situation, whether it is with a full stomach or empty, with plenty or little."*
>
> **Philippians 4:11b-12 (NLT)**

Three Ways to Learn Contentment

1. Stop _____.

> *"Peace of mind makes the body healthy, but jealousy is like a cancer."*
>
> **Proverbs 14:30 (TEV)**

2. Stop thinking that _____ is better.

3. Learn to _____ without having to _____.

> "I have the strength to face all conditions by the power that Christ gives me."
>
> **Philippians 4:13 (TEV)**

> "Obey God and be at peace with him; this is the way to happiness.
>
> **Job 22:21 (NCV)**

DISCOVERY QUESTIONS

1. Worry always exaggerates a problem. What problem are you experiencing that has only grown bigger with worry? Is it something you can change?

2. Pastor Rick encouraged you to talk to God about everything. In fact, if you prayed as much as you worry, you'd have a whole lot less to worry about. What do you need to talk to God about?

3. The war with stress is won or lost in your mind. What you fill your mind with will determine the level of stress in your life. What toxic thoughts have been polluting your mind?

4. Contentment is not based on circumstances. It's enjoying what you have right now rather than waiting for something else to make you happy. What have you been waiting for to make you happy?

5. Comparison is the source of all discontent. Have you caught yourself comparing lately? What have you been comparing, and what is it doing to your happiness?

6. You can admire something without having to acquire it. This helps create contentment. Do you own something that God is asking you to give away?

PUTTING IT INTO PRACTICE

The healthiest emotion human beings experience is gratitude. Expressing your gratitude on a daily basis is not only a powerful stress reliever; it also helps reduce anxiety and boost your mood. To begin developing your attitude of gratitude, find a small notepad or journal, and write down three things you are grateful for every day in the coming week.

PRAYER DIRECTION

Tell God that you want to make peace with him so you can reduce stress, experience his peace, and enjoy peace with others. You are ready to stop comparing and wanting more. Settle into contentment with the certainty you have the strength to face all conditions by the power of Christ.

FIVE DAILY HABITS
FOR HAPPINESS

CHECKING IN

Last week in session 5, you were encouraged to start a gratitude journal. How did this new habit change your stress level? Was it easy or difficult for you to think of three things you were grateful for each day? Share your thoughts with the group.

KEY VERSE

"All I want is to know Christ and to experience the power of his resurrection, to share in his sufferings and become like him in his death, in the hope that I myself will be raised from death to life."

Philippians 3:10-11 (TEV)

FIVE DAILY HABITS
FOR HAPPINESS

1. Every day: _____.

"We Christians glory in what Christ Jesus has done for us and realize that we are helpless to save ourselves."

Philippians 3:3b (TLB)

"We couldn't carry this off by our own efforts, and we know it."

Philippians 3:3 (MSG)

The Trap: _____

2. Every day: _____.

"Those things were important to me, but now I think they are worth nothing because of Christ."

Philippians 3:7 (NCV)

The Trap: _____

3. Every day: Get to know_____ better.

> "All I want is to know Christ and to experience the power of his resurrection, to share in his sufferings and become like him in his death, in the hope that I myself will be raised from death to life."
>
> **Philippians 3:10-11 (TEV)**

> "For my determined purpose is that I may know [Christ], that I may progressively become more deeply and intimately acquainted with Him, perceiving and recognizing and understanding the wonders of His Person more strongly and more clearly."
>
> **Philippians 3:10-11a (AMP)**

The Trap: _____

> "Be still, and know that I am God."
>
> **Psalm 46:10a (NIV)**

4. Every day: Review where I need to _____.

> *"Examine me, O God, and know my mind; test me, and discover my thoughts. Find out if there is any evil in me and guide me in the everlasting way."*
>
> **Psalm 139:23-24 (TEV)**

> *"I don't mean to say I am perfect. I haven't learned all I should even yet, but I keep working toward that day when I will finally be all that Christ saved me for and wants me to be. No, dear brothers, I am still not all I should be."*
>
> **Philippians 3:12-13a (TLB)**

The Trap: _____

5. Every day: Forget what can't be changed, and _____.

> *"I am bringing all my energies to bear on this one thing: Forgetting the past and looking forward to what lies ahead, I strain to reach the end of the race and receive the prize for which God is calling us up to heaven because of what Christ Jesus did for us."*
>
> **Philippians 3:13-14 (TLB)**

Three Traps to Avoid

1. _____

2. _____

3. _____

> *"Forget the former things and do not dwell on the past.*
> *See I am doing a new thing!"*
>
> **Isaiah 43:18-19 (NIV)**

DISCOVERY QUESTIONS

1. Accepting Christ and being in relationship with God changes you and your values. What things did you used to care about that really just don't matter anymore? What's important to you now?

2. You have to invest your time in a relationship to grow it. How much time do you spend getting to know Christ? If you aren't taking 10 to 15 minutes a day to do this, how can you reduce your busyness and make it a priority?

3. Pride will keep you from growing, but humility will lead to happiness, because it makes you teachable. When you are humble, you realize you don't have it all together, and you are eager to learn so you can be more like Christ. How is pride still getting in the way of your personal growth?

4. Happiness requires letting go and learning to forget. If you hold on to the pain of past hurts, it will steal your happiness. Decide now to stop letting the pain of your past control your happiness in the present. Ask people to share their experiences with living out this essential habit.

5. The reality is you have a limited supply of energy. Pastor Rick encourages you to use it on today and not waste any of it on the past. The past is past; it can't be changed. What hurt do you need to let go of? Share it with your group, and ask for their love, prayers, and support.

6. The only person you hurt with unforgiveness is you. It's time to forgive. Who do you need to forgive? Spend a few minutes in quiet reflection, considering the answer to this question. If you feel comfortable, share your thoughts with the group.

PUTTING IT INTO PRACTICE

Take a couple of minutes out of every day during your quiet time with God, and do a spiritual checkup. Take your spiritual pulse and do a spiritual EEG and EKG. Ask, "Lord, where do I need to grow? What do I need to work on? Where am I weak? Where do you want me to be stronger?"

PRAYER DIRECTION

Thank God for the wisdom you have gained from studying his Word and learning the habits of happiness. Ask him to help you keep making these truths a daily habit so you can worry less, pray more, reduce stress, and focus on what really matters.

SMALL GROUP RESOURCES

HELPS FOR HOSTS

TOP 10 IDEAS FOR NEW HOSTS

CONGRATULATIONS! As the host of your small group, you have responded to the call to help shepherd Jesus' flock. Few other tasks in the family of God surpass the contribution you will be making. As you prepare to facilitate your group, whether it is one session or the entire series, here are a few thoughts to keep in mind.

Remember you are not alone. God knows everything about you, and he knew you would be asked to facilitate your group. Even though you may not feel ready, this is common for all good hosts. God promises, *"I will never leave you; I will never abandon you"* (Hebrews 13:5 TEV). Whether you are facilitating for one evening, several weeks, or a lifetime, you will be blessed as you serve.

1. **DON'T TRY TO DO IT ALONE.** Pray right now for God to help you build a healthy team. If you can enlist a co-host to help you shepherd the group, you will find your experience much richer. This is your chance to involve as many people as you can in building a healthy group. All you have to do is ask people to help. You'll be surprised at the response.

2. **BE FRIENDLY AND BE YOURSELF.** God wants to use your unique gifts and temperament. Be sure to greet people at the door with a big smile . . . this can set the mood for the whole gathering. Remember, they are taking as big a step to show up at your house as you are to host a small group! Don't try to do things exactly like another host; do them in a way that fits you. Admit when you don't have an answer and apologize when you make a mistake. Your group will love you for it and you'll sleep better at night.

3. **PREPARE FOR YOUR MEETING AHEAD OF TIME**. Review the session and write down your responses to each question. Pay special attention to the Putting It Into Practice exercises that ask group members to do something other than engage in discussion. These exercises will help your group live what the Bible teaches, not just talk about it.

4. **PRAY FOR YOUR GROUP MEMBERS BY NAME.** Before you begin your session, take a few moments and pray for each member by name. You may want to review the Small Group Prayer and Praise Report at least once a week. Ask God to use your time together to touch the heart of each person in your group. Expect God to lead you to whomever he wants you to encourage or challenge in a special way. If you listen, God will surely lead.

5. **WHEN YOU ASK A QUESTION, BE PATIENT.** Someone will eventually respond. Sometimes people need a moment or two of silence to think about the question. If silence doesn't bother you, it won't bother anyone else. After someone responds, affirm the response with a simple "thanks" or "great answer." Then ask, "How about somebody else?" or "Would someone who hasn't shared like to add anything?" Be sensitive to new people or reluctant members who aren't ready to say, pray, or do anything. If you give them a safe setting, they will blossom over time. If someone in your group is a wallflower who sits silently through every session, consider talking to them privately and encouraging them to participate. Let them know how important they are to you—that they are loved and appreciated, and that the group would value their input. Remember, still water often runs deep.

6. **PROVIDE TRANSITIONS BETWEEN QUESTIONS.** Ask if anyone would like to read the paragraph or Bible passage. Don't call on anyone, but ask for a volunteer, and then be patient until someone begins. Be sure to thank the person who reads aloud.

7. **BREAK INTO SMALLER GROUPS OCCASIONALLY.** With a greater opportunity to talk in a small circle, people will connect more with the study, apply more quickly what they're learning, and ultimately get more out of their small group experience.

A small circle also encourages a quiet person to participate and tends to minimize the effects of a more vocal or dominant member.

8. **SMALL CIRCLES ARE ALSO HELPFUL DURING PRAYER TIME.** People who are unaccustomed to praying aloud will feel more comfortable trying it with just two or three others. Also, prayer requests won't take as much time, so circles will have more time to actually pray. When you gather back with the whole group, you can have one person from each circle briefly update everyone on the prayer requests from their subgroups. The other great aspect of subgrouping is that it fosters leadership development. As you ask people in the group to facilitate discussion or to lead a prayer circle, it gives them a small leadership step that can build their confidence.

9. **ROTATE FACILITATORS OCCASIONALLY.** You may be perfectly capable of hosting each time, but you will help others grow in their faith and gifts if you give them opportunities to host the group.

10. **ONE FINAL CHALLENGE (FOR NEW OR FIRST-TIME HOSTS).** Before your first opportunity to lead, look up each of the six passages listed below. Read each one as a devotional exercise to help prepare you with a shepherd's heart. Trust us on this one. If you do this, you will be more than ready for your first meeting.

> *[36]When Jesus saw the crowds, he had compassion on them, because they were harassed and helpless, like sheep without a shepherd. [37]Then he said to his disciples, "The harvest is plentiful but the workers are few. [38]Ask the Lord of the harvest, therefore, to send out workers into his harvest field."*
>
> **Matthew 9:36–38 (NIV)**

14I am the good shepherd; I know my sheep and my sheep know me—15just as the Father knows me and I know the Father—and I lay down my life for the sheep.

John 10:14–15 (NIV)

2Be shepherds of God's flock that is under your care, serving as overseers—not because you must, but because you are willing, as God wants you to be; 3not greedy for money, but eager to serve; not lording it over those entrusted to you, but being examples to the flock. 4And when the Chief Shepherd appears, you will receive the crown of glory that will never fade away.

1 Peter 5:2–4 (NIV)

1If you have any encouragement from being united with Christ, if any comfort from his love, if any fellowship with the Spirit, if any tenderness and compassion, 2then make my joy complete by being like-minded, having the same love, being one in spirit and purpose. 3Do nothing out of selfish ambition or vain conceit, but in humility consider others better than yourselves. 4Each of you should look not only to your own interests, but also to the interests of others. 5Your attitude should be the same as that of Jesus Christ.

Philippians 2:1–5 (NIV)

23Let us hold unswervingly to the hope we profess, for he who promised is faithful. 24And let us consider how we may spur one another on toward love and good deeds. 25Let us not give up meeting together, as some are in the habit of doing, but let us encourage one another—and all the more as you see the Day approaching.

Hebrews 10:23–25 (NIV)

[7]...but we were gentle among you, like a mother caring for her little children. [8]We loved you so much that we were delighted to share with you not only the gospel of God but our lives as well, because you had become so dear to us.... [11]For you know that we dealt with each of you as a father deals with his own children, [12]encouraging, comforting and urging you to live lives worthy of God, who calls you into his kingdom and glory.

1 Thessalonians 2:7–8, 11–12 (NIV)

FREQUENTLY ASKED QUESTIONS

How long will this group meet?

This study is six sessions long. We encourage your group to add a seventh session for a celebration. In your final session, each group member may decide if he or she desires to continue on for another study. At that time you may also want to do some informal evaluation, discuss your group guidelines, and decide which study you want to do next. We recommend you visit our website at saddlebackresources.com for more video-based small group studies.

Who is the host?

The host is the person who coordinates and facilitates your group meetings. In addition to a host, we encourage you to select one or more group members to lead your group discussions. Several other responsibilities can be rotated, including refreshments, prayer requests, worship, or keeping up with those who miss a meeting. Shared ownership in the group helps everybody grow.

Where do we find new group members?

Recruiting new members can be a challenge for groups, especially new groups with just a few people, or existing groups that lose a few people along the way. We encourage you to use the Circles of Life diagram on page 68 of this study guide to brainstorm a list of people from your workplace, church, school, neighborhood, family, and so on. Then pray for the people on each member's list. Allow each member to invite several people from their list. Some groups fear that newcomers will interrupt the intimacy that members have built over time. However, groups that welcome newcomers generally gain strength with the infusion of new blood. Remember, the next person you add just might become a friend for eternity. Logistically, groups find different ways to add members. Some groups remain permanently open, while others choose to open periodically, such as at the beginning or end of a study. If your group becomes too large for easy, face-to-face conversations, you can subgroup, forming a second discussion group in another room.

How do we handle the childcare needs in our group?

Childcare needs must be handled very carefully. This is a sensitive issue. We suggest you seek creative solutions as a group. One common solution is to have the adults meet in the living room and share the cost of a babysitter (or two) who can be with the kids in another part of the house.

Another popular option is to have one home for the kids and a second home (close by) for the adults. If desired, the adults could rotate the responsibility of providing a lesson for the kids. This last option is great with school-age kids and can be a huge blessing to families.

CIRCLES OF LIFE

Discover Who You Can Connect in Community

Use this chart to help carry out one of the values in the Group Guidelines, to "Welcome Newcomers."

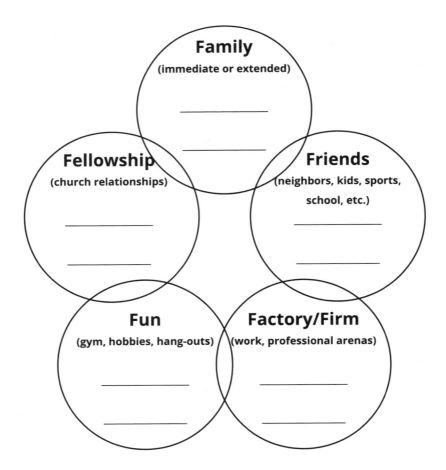

68

Follow this simple three-step process:

1. List one to two people in each circle.

2. Prayerfully select one person or couple from your list and tell your group about them.

3. Give them a call and invite them to your next meeting. Over fifty percent of those invited to a small group say, "Yes!"

GROUP GUIDELINES

It's a good idea for every group to put words to their shared values, expectations, and commitments. Such guidelines will help you avoid unspoken agendas and unmet expectations. We recommend you discuss your guidelines during Session 1 in order to lay the foundation for a healthy group experience. Feel free to modify anything that does not work for your group.

We agree to the following values:

CLEAR PURPOSE	To grow healthy spiritual lives by building a healthy small group community
GROUP ATTENDANCE	To give priority to the group meeting (call if I am absent or late)
SAFE ENVIRONMENT	To create a safe place where people can be heard and feel loved (no quick answers, snap judgments, or simple fixes)
BE CONFIDENTIAL	To keep anything that is shared strictly confidential and within the group

CONFLICT RESOLUTION	To avoid gossip and to immediately resolve any concerns by following the principles of Matthew 18:15–17
SPIRITUAL HEALTH	To give group members permission to speak into my life and help me live a healthy, balanced spiritual life that is pleasing to God
LIMIT OUR FREEDOM	To limit our freedom by not serving or consuming alcohol during small group meetings or events so as to avoid causing a weaker brother or sister to stumble (1 Corinthians 8:1–13; Romans 14:19–21)
WELCOME NEWCOMERS	To invite friends who might benefit from this study and warmly welcome newcomers
BUILDING RELATIONSHIPS	To get to know the other members of the group and pray for them regularly
OTHER	_____ _____ _____

We have also discussed and agree on the following items:

CHILD CARE   _____

STARTING TIME   _____

ENDING TIME   _____

If you haven't already done so, take a few minutes to fill out the Small Group Calendar on page 74.

SMALL GROUP PRAYER AND PRAISE REPORT

This is a place where you can write each other's requests for prayer. You can also make a note when God answers a prayer. Pray for each other's requests. If you're new to group prayer, it's okay to pray silently or to pray by using just one sentence:

"God, please help _____ to _____ ."

DATE	PERSON	PRAYER REQUEST	PRAISE REPORT

DATE	PERSON	PRAYER REQUEST	PRAISE REPORT

SMALL GROUP CALENDAR

Healthy groups share responsibilities and group ownership. It might take some time for this to develop. Shared ownership ensures that responsibility for the group doesn't fall to one person. Use the calendar to keep track of social events, mission projects, birthdays, or days off. Complete this calendar at your first or second meeting. Planning ahead will increase attendance and shared ownership.

DATE	LESSON	LOCATION	FACILITATOR	SNACK OR MEAL
	Session 1			
	Session 2			
	Session 3			

DATE	LESSON	LOCATION	FACILITATOR	SNACK OR MEAL
	Session 4			
	Session 5			
	Session 6			
	Celebration			

ANSWER KEY

SESSION 1:

GROWING HEALTHY RELATIONSHIPS

Five Laws of Happiness

1. Don't look for happiness; **create it**.
2. Happiness is not **a goal**.
3. **My habits** create my happiness.
4. Happiness based on happenings is **temporary**. But happiness built on habits is **longlasting**.
5. **Happy** habits are as addicting as bad habits.

Four Relational Habits of Happiness

1. I must **be grateful** for the people in my life.

   Happiness Hint: Remember **the best**, and **forget the rest**.

2. **Pray with joy** for the people in my life.

   Happiness Hint: The quickest way to change a bad relationship to a good one, **start praying for them**.

Four Things to Pray for People

- They will **grow in love**.
- They will **make wise choices**.
- They will **live with integrity**.
- They will **become like Jesus**.

3. **Expect the best** from people in my life.

Three Ways Paul Brought the Best Out of People

- He **believed in people**.
- He **gave people vision**.
- He was **patient with people's progress**.

Happiness Hint: Celebrate **how far people have come** rather than judging them for **how far they still have to go**.

4. Love people in my life **like Jesus does**.

76

SESSION 2:

HOW TO BE HAPPY NO MATTER WHAT

Four Common Barriers to Happiness

1. **Pain**
2. **People**
3. **Pressure**
4. **Problems**

You can be happy if you...

1. Look at every problem from **God's viewpoint**.

Any time you face problems in faith:

- It's a **witness to unbelievers**.
- It's an **encouragement to believers**.
2. Never let others **control my attitude**.

Four Kinds of People

Happiness Hint: **I don't need other people's approval to be happy**.

3. **Always trust God** to work things out.

Four Sources of Strength

1. I have God's **perspective** on my problems.
2. I have people **praying** for me.
3. I have the **Holy Spirit** helping me.
4. I have faith that **God will work it for good**.

4. If I stay **focused on my purpose**, not my problem.

SESSION 3:
THE HUMBLE PATH TO HAPPINESS
Four Kinds of Harmony

1. **Mental**
2. **Emotional**
3. **Spiritual**
4. **Directional**

Four Habits for Reducing Conflict

1. Never let **my pride** be my guide.
2. Be **humble**, or I'll stumble!
3. Learn the lost art of **paying attention**!
4. Ask, "What would **Jesus** do?"

Three Examples of Acting Like Jesus

1. **Don't demand** what I think I deserve.
2. 2. Look for ways that I can **serve**.
3. **Do what's right** even when it's painful.

SESSION 4:
HOW TO KEEP YOUR HEART HAPPY
Five Exercises for a Happy Heart

1. Remember that God is **with** me, he's **in** me, and he's **for** me.
2. **Be grateful** and **never grumble**.
3. Keep my **conscience** clear.
4. **Memorize** God's Word and **live it**.
5. Use my life **to serve God** by serving others.

SESSION 5:

HOW TO KEEP FROM STRESSING OUT

Ways to Keep from Stressing Out

1. **Refuse to worry** about anything.

Four Reasons You Should Never Worry About Anything

1. Worry is **unreasonable**.
2. Worry is **unnatural**.
3. Worry is **unhelpful**.
4. Worry is **unnecessary**.

2. **Talk to God** about everything.

3. **Thank God** in all things.

4. Think about **good things**.

5. **Be content** with anything.

Three Ways to Learn Contentment

1. Stop **comparing**.
2. Stop thinking that **having more** is better.
3. Learn to **admire** without having to **acquire**.

SESSION 6:

FIVE DAILY HABITS FOR HAPPINESS

1. Every day: **Relax in God's grace.**

   The Trap: **Legalism**

2. Every day: **Remember what matters most**.

   The Trap: **Popular culture**

3. Every day: Get to know **Jesus** better.

   The Trap: **Busyness**

4. Every day: Review where I need to **grow**.

   The Trap: **Pride**

5. Every day: Forget what can't be changed, and **focus on the future**.

Three Traps to Avoid

1. **Regret**
2. **Unforgiveness or resentment**
3. **Tradition**